GREEN
Is a
CHILE PEPPER

El chile
es
verde

To Maya, who loves chile peppers on everything imaginable! —R. G. T.

To my aunts: Eleanor, Marie, Joan, Mary, Nancy, and Patricia, for all your love and support. —J. P.

A Maya, ¡a quien le encanta ponerle chiles a todo! —R. G. T.

A mis tías: Eleanor, Marie, Joan, Nancy y Patricia, por todo su amor y apoyo —J. P.

Originally published in English as *Green Is a Chile Pepper* by Chronicle Books LLC.

Text © 2014 by Roseanne Greenfield Thong.
Illustrations copyright © 2014 by John Parra.
Spanish translation copyright © 2015 by Scholastic Inc.

ISBN 978-0-545-86868-6

10 9 8 7 6 5 4 3 2 1   15 16 17 18 19/0

Printed in the U.S.A.   40
First Scholastic bilingual printing, September 2015

Book design by Amelia Mack and Eloise Leigh.
Typeset in Brandon Grotesque.
The illustrations in this book were rendered in paint.

GREEN Is a CHILE PEPPER
El chile es verde

A Book of Colors
Un libro de colores

Roseanne Greenfield Thong
Illustrated by/*Ilustrado por* John Parra

SCHOLASTIC INC.

Red is a *ristra*.
 Red is a spice.
Red is our *salsa*
 on top of rice.

Roja es una ristra.
Rojo es un condimento.
Roja es la salsa
que servimos con el arroz.

red • rojo

Red is a ribbon.
Red is a bow
and skirts for
baile folclórico.

Roja es una cinta.
Rojo es un lazo
y rojas son las faldas
del baile folclórico.

Orange are the marigolds
on Day of the Dead.
Orange are the *platos*
for special bread.

Naranja son las caléndulas
del Día de los Muertos.
Naranja son los platos
para los panes especiales.

orange ◉ naranja

Yellow is *masa*
we use to make
tortillas, tamales, and
sweet corn cake!

*Amarilla es la masa
que usamos para hacer
tortillas, tamales
¡y el pan de elote!*

yellow ☀ amarillo

Yellow are the stars
that lighten the night.
Yellow are *faroles*
flickering bright.

*Amarillas son las estrellas
que iluminan la noche.
Amarillos son los faroles
que brillan y parpadean.*

yellow ⦿ amarillo

Green are the cornstalks.
Green are the pails.
Green is a bench
   for abuela's tales.

Verdes son los tallos del maíz.
Verdes son los baldes.
Verde es el banco
para las historias de la abuela.

green ☼ verde

Green is a chile pepper,
spicy and hot.
Green is cilantro
inside our pot.

Verde es el chile,
sabroso y picante.
Verde es el cilantro
que va en nuestra olla.

green ☼ verde

Blue is the endless sky above
and handmade crafts for those I love.

Azul es el cielo infinito allá arriba
y las artesanías para nuestros seres queridos.

blue ☀ azul

Purple are the rides
that swirl and spin
and the *feria* prizes
that we win.

*Púrpura son las atracciones
que giran y dan vueltas
y los premios que ganamos
en la feria.*

CARNIVAL

purple ☀ púrpura

Pink are *adornos*
and candles that glow.
Pink are *piñatas*:
Watch out below!

*Rosa son los adornos
y las velas que brillan.
Rosa son las piñatas:
¡Tengan cuidado!*

pink ⚬ rosa

Brown is a *churro*,
   warm and sweet,
and homemade *chocolate*
   —a special treat.

Marrón es el churro,
calentito y dulce,
y el chocolate casero,
una merienda especial.

brown ❁ marrón

white ◦ blanco

White are the flowers
    we put in a vase,
and sugar skulls
    and handmade lace.

Blancas son las flores
que ponemos en el florero,
y las calaveras de dulce
y el encaje hecho a mano.

White are the doves
    that chatter and coo,
and the *palomitas*
    for me and you.

Blancas son las palomas
que charlan y arrullan,
y las palomitas de maíz
para ti y para mí.

white ⚪ *blanco*

The world is a rainbow of wonder and fun:
ribbons of colors rolled into one.

*El mundo es un arcoíris de maravillas y diversión:
cintas de colores que se vuelven una sola.*

In *ponchos*, *sarapes*, and xylophones, too,
these beautiful colors are waiting for you!

En ponchos, sarapes y xilófonos también,
¡estos lindos colores esperan por ti!

GLOSSARY

ADORNOS: Decorations.

BAILE FOLCLÓRICO: Mexican folk dancing, known for heel stomping and swirling skirts.

CHILES: Chiles come in many colors, including green, red, orange, yellow, and purple. Two popular *chiles* are *poblanos* and *jalapeños*.

CHURROS: Long, thin doughnut-like snacks that are fried until crunchy and sprinkled with cinnamon sugar.

FAROLES: Lanterns made of colorful paper with a lit candle inside.

FERIA: A carnival that often includes rodeos, rides, food stalls, and game booths for winning prizes.

MASA: A cornmeal dough used for foods like *tamales* and *tortillas*.

PALOMITAS: Meaning "little doves," it is also the word for popcorn.

PLATOS: Plates or serving dishes.

RISTRA: Bundles of red chiles that often hang on long strings in Mexican kitchens.

SARAPE: A long, rectangular piece of wool worn around the shoulders or used as a blanket.